# THE GREAT AND MIGHTY WALL

This is a story that happened over a thousand years ago

In Ancient Yoruba Land at a place called Eredö

There lived a great and wonderful Queen that you may or may not know

And the name of that great and wonderful Queen, was Queen Bilikisu Sungbo

Queen Bilikisu as she was known, was kind and generous

And the kingdom that she ruled over, was very prosperous

The buildings in her kingdom, were beautifully made

And people came from far and wide to this kingdom, just so they could trade

Her father the King was a wise man and was known as the Great King

He was always kind to his subjects, who in turn looked up to him

He dwelled in a large court, with his courtiers by his side

Who were always happy to serve him, with honour, respect and pride

Even though Queen Bilikisu was surrounded by people,

there were times she felt alone

She felt sad when watching the children play, as she longed for children of her own

But what made Queen Bilikisu even sadder, was her kingdom being under attack

By lions that were trained by her rivals, she knew she had to put a stop to that

These attacks would happen at night, which left her people terrified and grieving

So much so that from her kingdom, her people they started leaving

Queen Bilikisu walked through her kingdom and did not like what she saw

The destruction caused by the raiding lions, just saddened her even more

So she summoned all her advisors and all the elders too

To join her in a meeting, to discuss what they could do

The advisor who was the town planner suggested, they move the kingdom away

"Relocate all the people" he said, "find a new place to stay"

But Queen Bilikisu disagreed and said, "This is where we have always been

It would disrupt our trade links with the other countries, plus the land is so fertile

and green!"

The advisor who was the first knight suggested, that they all should take up arms

"Kill every lion that enters the kingdom" he said, "so they can no longer cause any harm"

But Queen Bilikisu turned to the first knight and said, "I cannot agree with you

It's not the fault of the lions, they're only doing what they were trained to do!"

The meeting ended without anyone, coming up with a good solution

The advisors and elders left the Queen by herself, to come up with her own resolution

Queen Bilikisu was determined to solve the problem, but she knew it would be very hard

So in order to clear her thoughts she decided to take a walk in the court yard

It was there in the court yard it came to her, how she could save them all

"I know what to do, I'll surround my kingdom with a Great and Mighty Wall"

She summoned her advisors and elders

again, to tell them about what she had planned

But they all disagreed, they thought that she was mad and they

just could not understand

How could it be possible to build a wall, to surround a kingdom so big

"The Great and Mighty Wall will be built!" she said, and that's what the Queen insisted!

When people from all over heard the news of the wall,

to help they were all very keen

They came to the court bringing gifts of all sorts, to help raise money for the Queen

They brought iron and brass and gold and silver, they even brought food and wine

And when all that was sold and the money was raised, Queen Bilikisu said, "It is time"

With no time to waste, no time to stall

They started to construct the Great and Mighty Wall

For extra security a moat was built too

Just to make sure, no lions could get through

When the advisors and elders came to check the progress

They made it clear to Queen Bilikisu, that they were not impressed

Queen Bilikisu said, "Impressing you is not what it's about

This wall is being built to keep our enemies out"

The work was continuous, there was no time to stop

The wall was built strong from bottom to top

Row by row, brick by brick

70ft high and 12ft thick

After 18 moons it was finally done

The Great and Mighty Wall was second to none

The kingdom was now safe, from any attack

And the people knew the lions would never come back

If you want to visit the wall then I'm pleased to say

The Great and Mighty Wall still stands today

In that beautiful place known as Eredö

Where the people still speak of Queen Bilikisu Sungbo

THE END

The facts of this story are:

Queen Bilikisu Sungbo lived over a thousand years ago between 800 and 1000 AD

Queen Bilikisu Sungbo is sometimes mistaken for the Queen of Sheba,
who was also known as 'Bilqis'

Some say Bilikisu and Bilqis is the same person, but we believe that this is not possible
because the Queen of Sheba, aka Bilqis lived approximately 1000BC, which is two thousand
years before Queen Bilikisu Sungbo

Ancient Yoruba Land was located in what is now known as modern day Nigeria

Eredö is located approximately 60 miles from Lagos, where you can go to see
'The Great and Mighty Wall'